G000114423

Macbeth

The story of *Macbeth* is more legend than history. And Macbeth's Scotland is a country of the imagination rather than a geographical location. Nevertheless, it is generally agreed that Shakespeare wrote the play in 1606 for performance at Hampton Court before the then recently crowned king of England, James I. And, coincidentally, it focuses on a number of King James's particular interests. For one, his passion for Scotland, his native country, and its past, was well known. So, too, was his interest in witchcraft, and, in fact, he was considered something of an authority on the subject, having published a book, *Daemonology*, in 1603, the year of his coronation.

The three "weird sisters" of Scottish legend have at various times been presented as goddesses of destiny, as nymphs, and as fairies. Shakespeare, however, portrays them in *Macbeth* as traditional Scottish witches: old and wizened hags with hairy chins and malevolent laughter. And they are also of central importance to the play, illustrating as they do the struggle between the individual and the powers of darkness.

The precise extent of their influence over Macbeth is unclear. The English poet, W.H. Auden, has said that if Macbeth had listened to the witches' prophecy as a Greek would have listened to the Oracle, then he would have been able to sit and wait until it came to pass. Instead,

Macbeth makes a series of wrong moves, believing his acts to be his own. When he comes to believe that he can do whatever he pleases, irrespective of God's will, the tragedy ensues.

Macbeth was first performed in 1606

Macbeth

The scene is a wild, windswept Scottish heath. Three wizened old witches are gathered, discussing a forthcoming encounter with Macbeth, a Scottish general.

FIRST WITCH: When shall we three meet again?
In thunder, lightning, or in rain?

SECOND WITCH: When the hurly-burly's done,
When the battle's lost and won.

THIRD WITCH: That will be ere set of sun.

FIRST WITCH: Where the place?

SECOND WITCH: Upon the heath.

THIRD WITCH: There to meet with Macbeth.

ALL: Fair is foul and foul is fair,
Hover through the fog and the filthy air.

Meanwhile, the battle for Scotland itself is being fought. Sweno, king of Norway, has invaded, aided and abetted by Macdonald of the Western Isles and the Thane, or Lord, of Cawdor. The two Scottish generals, Macbeth and Banquo, lead the charge against them and, after much fierce fighting, emerge victorious. When reports of their heroism reach Duncan, the king of Scotland, he orders that the treacherous Thane of Cawdor be put to death and that Macbeth be awarded his title:

KING: No more that Thane of Cawdor shall deceive
Our bosom interest. Go pronounce his present death,
And with his former title greet Macbeth.

ROSS: I'll see it done.

KING: What he hath lost, noble Macbeth has won.

As Macbeth and Banquo return from the battle, they find their way over the heathland barred by the three witches, who make some startling predictions about Macbeth's future.

BANQUO: What are these,
So withered and so wild in their attire,
That look not like the inhabitants of the earth,
And yet are on't? Live you? Or are you aught
That man may question? You seem to understand me
By each at once her choppy finger laying
Upon her skinny lips. You should be women,
And yet your beards forbid me to interpret
That you are so.

MACBETH: Speak if you can! What are you?

FIRST WITCH: All hail, Macbeth! Hail to thee, Thane of Glamis!

SECOND WITCH: All hail, Macbeth! Hail to thee, Thane of Cawdor!

Macbeth is intrigued, not only to find himself known by such creatures but also because they salute him as Thane of Cawdor, since news of his new title has not yet reached him. He is still more surprised when saluted by the third witch:

THIRD WITCH: All hail, Macbeth, that shalt be king hereafter!

They then turn to Banquo, and prophesy that he will be much happier than Macbeth, and that he will produce heirs who, in their turn, will also become kings. The witches then prepare to leave.

MACBETH: Stay, you imperfect speakers! Tell me more!

By Sinell's death I know I am Thane of Glamis;
But how of Cawdor? The Thane of Cawdor lives
A prosperous gentleman. And to be king
Stands not within the prospect of belief -
No more than to be Cawdor. Say from whence
You owe this strange intelligence, or why
Upon this blasted heath you stop our way
With such prophetic greeting? Speak, I charge you!

Without responding, the witches vanish into the air, but no sooner have they gone than two thanes, Ross and Angus, messengers from the King, arrive.

ROSS: The King hath happily received, Macbeth,
The news of thy success.

ANGUS: We are sent
To give thee from our royal master thanks.

ROSS: And, for an earnest of a greater honour,
He bade me from him call thee Thane of Cawdor
In which addition, hail, most worthy thane,
For it is thine.

BANQUO: (*aside*) What! Can the devil speak true?

Macbeth is startled that part of the witches' prophecy has proved accurate, and that it has happened so quickly. He begins to ponder what the future may have in store:

MACBETH: Glamis, and Thane of Cawdor! Two truths are told
As happy prologues to the swelling act

Of the imperial theme ...
If chance will have me king, why chance may crown
me
Without my stir ... Come what come may,
Time and the hour runs through the roughest day.

Arriving at the king's palace, Macbeth and Banquo learn the king intends to further honor Macbeth by visiting him and staying at his castle in Inverness. Macbeth conveys all this to his wife in a letter. Although buoyed by the news, Lady Macbeth is afraid her husband is too weak to quickly find his way to the throne. She plots how she can work him into doing evil to gain the crown.

Lady Macbeth: Glamis thou art, and Cawdor, and shalt
be
What thou art promised. Yet do I fear thy nature:
It is too full of the milk of human kindness
To catch the nearest way. Thou wouldst be great,
Art not without ambition, but without
The illness should attend it ...

Before Macbeth arrives back at Inverness, Lady Macbeth invokes the powers of darkness to strengthen her resolve to have the king killed.

Lady Macbeth: Come, you spirits
That tend on mortal thoughts, unsex me here

And fill me from the crown to the toe top-full
Of direst cruelty.

When Macbeth arrives home and confirms the imminent arrival of King Duncan at the castle, he is unaware of his wife's murderous plans. However, Lady Macbeth wastes no time in trying to persuade her husband to undertake her scheme by stressing the reward he will reap - the crown.

MACBETH: My dearest love,
Duncan comes here tonight.

LADY MACBETH: And when goes hence?

MACBETH: Tomorrow, as he proposes.

LADY MACBETH: O never
Shall sun that morrow see!
Your face, my thane, is as a book where men
May read strange matters. To beguile the time
Look like the time, bear welcome in your eye,
Your hand, your tongue; look like the innocent flower,
But be the serpent under't. He that's coming
Must be provided for; and you shall put
This night's great business into my despatch,
Which shall to all our nights and days to come
Give solely sovereign sway and masterdom.

MACBETH: We will speak further.

The unsuspecting King Duncan, his sons, Malcolm and Donalbain, and his entourage arrive at Inverness later the same day and are warmly welcomed by Lady Macbeth. In the evening a banquet is held in the king's honor, during which Macbeth - who has doubts about the plot to murder the king - excuses himself; anguishing over the task ahead.

MACBETH: If it were done when 'tis done, then 'twere well
It were done quickly. If the assassination
Could trammel up the consequence, and catch
With his surcease success - that but this blow
Might be the be-all and the end-all! ...
He's here in double trust:
First, as I am his kinsman and his subject,
Strong both against the deed; then, as his host,
Who should against his murderer shut the door,
Not bear the knife myself.

Lady Macbeth follows him out of the banquet room and they argue. Macbeth does not want to proceed with the murder, but Lady Macbeth goads and manipulates him until he agrees.

MACBETH: We will proceed no further in this business,

He hath honoured me of late, and I have bought
Golden opinions from all sorts of people
Which would be worn now in their newest gloss,
Not cast aside so soon.

LADY MACBETH: Was the hope drunk
Wherein you dressed yourself? Hath it slept since?
And wakes it now to look so green and pale
At what it did so freely... Art thou afeard
To be the same in thine own act and valour
As thou art in desire?

MACBETH: Prithee peace,
I dare do all that may become a man
Who does more is none.

LADY MACBETH: What beast was it then
That made you break this enterprise to me?

MACBETH: If we should fail?

LADY MACBETH: We fail!
But screw your courage to the sticking place,
And we'll not fail...

MACBETH: I am settled, and bend up
Each corporal agent to this terrible feat.
Away and mock the time with fairest show:

False face must hide what false heart doth know.

Later, everyone retires to bed except Macbeth. In the darkness he prowls the corridors of the castle, brooding over his imminent action.

MACBETH: Is this a dagger which I see before me,
The handle toward my hand? Come, let me clutch thee:
I have thee not and yet I see thee still.
Art thou not, fatal vision, sensible
To feeling as to sight? Or art thou but
A dagger of the mind, a false creation,
Proceeding from the heat-oppressed brain?...
Thou sure and firm-set earth,
Hear not my steps, which way they walk, for fear
Thy very stones prate of my whereabout

And take the present horror from the time
Which now suits with it. While I threat, he lives:
Words to the heat of deeds too cold breath gives.

A bell rings.

MACBETH: I go, and it is done. The bell invites me.
Hear it not, Duncan, for it is a knell
That summons thee to heaven or to hell.

Lady Macbeth, meanwhile, has drugged the drinks of Duncan's servants and, slightly intoxicated herself after the feasting, waits for her husband in her chamber. He arrives carrying two bloody daggers.

LADY MACBETH: My husband!

MACBETH: I have done the deed. Didst thou hear a noise?

Macbeth stares in horror at his blood-stained hands.

LADY MACBETH: Go, get some water,
And wash this filthy witness from your hand.
Why did you bring these daggers from the place?
They must lie there. Go, carry them and smear
The sleepy grooms with blood.

MACBETH: I'll go no more.
I am afraid to think what I have done.

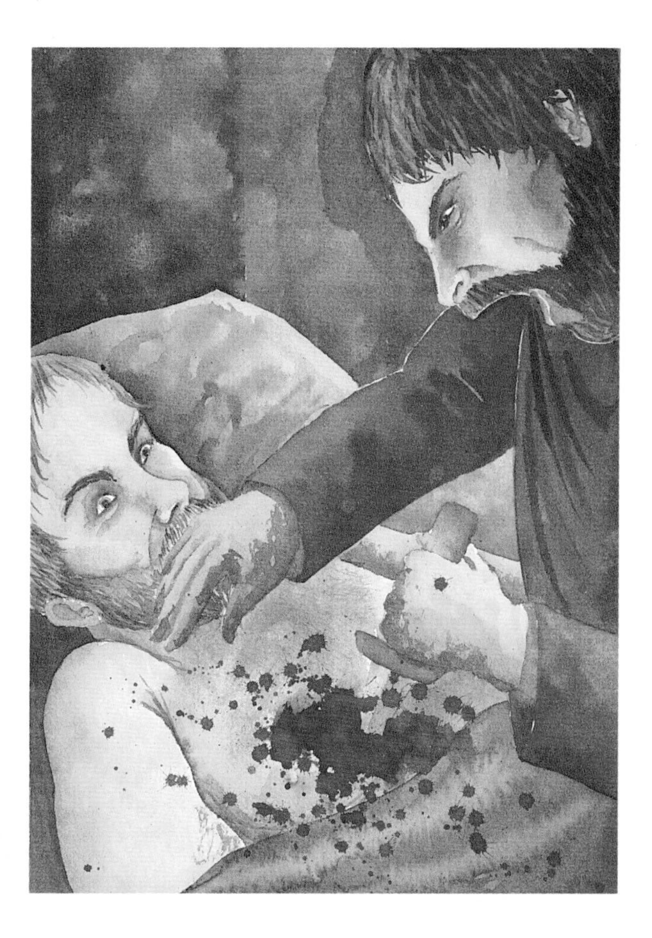

LADY MACBETH: Give me the daggers. The sleeping and the dead
Are but as pictures. 'Tis the eye of childhood
That fears a painted devil. If he do bleed
I'll gild the faces of the grooms withal,
For it must seem their guilt.

Lady Macbeth grabs the daggers and goes off to leave them at the scene of the crime. Meanwhile there is a loud knock on the castle door.

MACBETH: Whence is that knocking?
How is't with me when every noise appals me?
What hands are here! Ah, they pluck out mine eyes!
Will all great Neptune's ocean wash this blood
Clean from my hand? No, this my hand will rather
The multitudinous seas incarnadine,
Making the green one red.

Once again comes the knock.

Lady Macbeth: I hear a knocking
At the south entry. Retire we to our chamber.
A little water clears us of this deed.
How easy is it then!

The knock comes for a third time.

LADY MACBETH: Hark! More knocking.
Get on your nightgown, lest occasion call us
And show us to be watches. Be not lost
So poorly in your thoughts.

The knocking on the castle door continues incessantly,

until eventually an old porter stirs himself from his drunken sleep and opens it. At the door are the two thanes, Macduff and Lennox, come to rouse the king.

MACDUFF: Is the king stirring, worthy thane?

MACBETH: Not yet.

MACDUFF: He did command me to call timely on him.
I have almost slipped the hour.

MACBETH: I'll bring you to him.

Macduff goes to the king's bedchamber to wake him,

but returns, white and shaken:

MACDUFF: Ring the alarum bell! Murder and treason!
Banquo and Donalbain, Malcolm, awake!
Shake off this downy sleep, death's counterfeit,
And look on death itself!

The mayhem and uproar that follows the discovery of the dead king brings the other guests from their rooms.

DONALBAIN: What is amiss!

MACDUFF: Your royal father's murdered.

MALCOLM: O! By whom?

LENNOX: Those of his chamber, as it seemed, have done it.

Their hands and faces were all badged with blood,
So were their daggers which, unwiped, we found
Upon their pillows.

Macbeth announces to the company that he has killed Duncan's servants, who must have been responsible for the king's murder. The king's sons now become fearful for their own safety, and decide to flee Scotland:

MALCOLM: What will you do? Let's not consort with them.
To show an unfelt sorrow is an office
Which the false man does easy. I'll to England.

DONALBAIN: To Ireland, I. Our separate fortune
Shall keep us both the safer. Where we are
There's daggers in men's smiles. The nearer in blood,
The nearer bloody.

The flight of Malcolm and Donalbain leaves Macbeth as the next heir to the Scottish throne, and he is crowned king. Banquo, suspicious of Macbeth, recalls the witches' prophecy:

BANQUO: *(to himself)* Thou hast it now: King, Cawdor, Glamis, all
As the weird women promised; and I fear
Thou playedst most foully for it.

Nor has Macbeth forgotten the witches' prediction; has he, he asks himself, come this far merely to pass the crown on to Banquo's heirs?

MACBETH: If it be so,
For Banquo's issue have I filed my mind,
For them the gracious Duncan have I murdered,
But rancours in the vessel of my peace,
Only for them; and mine eternal jewel
Given to the common enemy of man,
To make them kings, the seed of Banquo kings!

Macbeth arranges to have Banquo and his son, Fleance, murdered that very day. He arranges for two villains to ambush them.

MACBETH: Within this hour, at most,
I will advise you where to plant yourselves,
Acquaint you with the perfect spy o' the time,
The moment on't. For't must be done tonight...

Macbeth has become completely obsessed with his power. Lady Macbeth urges him to calm down and get ready for the banquet that they, now King and Queen, have planned for the Scottish nobility.

LADY MACBETH: Come on,
Gentle my lord, sleek o'er your rugged looks,

Be bright and jovial among your guests tonight.

MACBETH: O, full of scorpions is my mind, dear wife!
Thou know'st that Banquo and his Fleance lives.

LADY MACBETH: What's to be done?

MACBETH: Be innocent of the knowledge, dearest chuck,
Till thou applaud the deed. Come, seeling night,
Scarf up the tender eye of pitiful day,
And with thy bloody and invisible hand
Cancel and tear to pieces that great bond
Which keeps me pale. Light thickens
And the crow makes wing to the rooky wood.
Good things of day begin to droop and drowse,
While night's black agents to their preys do rouse.
Thou marvel'st at my words, but hold thee still.
Things bad begun make strong themselves by ill.

Meanwhile, Banquo and Fleance are ambushed. Banquo is killed but Fleance escapes. One of the murderers arrives to tell Macbeth, just as the banquet begins.

MURDERER: My lord, his throat is cut.
That I did for him.

MACBETH: Thou art the best o' the cut-throats,
Yet he's good that did the like for Fleance.

MURDERER: Most royal Sir, Fleance is escaped.

Learning that Fleance has escaped unnerves Macbeth, but he must turn his attention to his guests.

MACBETH: Sweet remembrancer!
Now good digestion wait on appetite.
And health on both!

LENNOX: May it please your highness, sit.

Just at this point the ghost of Banquo enters the banquet chamber, unseen by all but Macbeth, and sits down at Macbeth's own place. Macbeth turns pale with shock:

MACBETH: Which of you have done this?

LORDS: What, my good lord?

MACBETH: Thou canst not say I did it. Never shake
Thy gory locks at me.

ROSS: Gentlemen, rise. His highness is not well.

LADY MACBETH: Sit, worthy friends. My lord is often thus,
And hath been from his youth. Pray you keep seat.

MACBETH: Prithee, see there!
Behold! Look! Lo! How say you?
Why, what care I if thou can'st nod! Speak, too!

The ghost vanishes and Macbeth, suddenly aware of the effect his bizarre behavior is having on his guests, tries to recover his composure.

MACBETH: I do forget.
Do not muse at me, my most worthy friends,
I have a strange infirmity, which is nothing
To those that know me. Come, love and health to all!
Then I'll sit down. Give me some wine. Fill full!

But at this the ghost re-enters the room, and again only Macbeth sees it. Once more he is overcome and Lady Macbeth dismisses the guests.

LADY MACBETH: I pray you speak not; he grows worse and worse,
Question enrages him. At once, good night.
Stand not upon the order of your going,

But go at once.

LENNOX: Good night, and better health
Attend his majesty!

LADY MACBETH: A kind good-night to all!

When all the guests have departed, Macbeth tells his wife of his forebodings. He intends to seek out the witches the next day to find out what further prophecies they have for his future.

MACBETH: It will have blood, they say; blood will have blood...
I will tomorrow -
And betimes I will - to the Weird sisters.
More shall they speak, for now I am bent to know
By the worst means the worst. For mine own good
All causes shall give way.

The next day, Macbeth finds the weird sisters in a cave on the heath. They are busy preparing a foul concoction in a large cauldron.

FIRST WITCH: Round about the cauldron go,
In the poisoned entrails throw.
Toad that under cold stone
Days and nights has thirty-one.

Sweltered venom, sleeping got,
Boil thou first in the charmed pot.

ALL: Double, double, toil and trouble,
Fire burn, and cauldron bubble.

SECOND WITCH: Fillet of a fenny snake

In the cauldron boil and bake.
Eye of newt, and toe of frog,
Wool of bat, and tongue of dog,
Adder's fork, and blind worm's sting,
Lizard's leg and howlets wing.
For a charm of powerful trouble,
Like a hell-broth, boil and bubble.

ALL: Double, double, toil and trouble;
Fire burn and cauldron bubble.

THIRD WITCH: Liver of blaspheming Jew,
Gall of goat, and ships of yew
Slivered in the moon's eclipse,
Nose of Turk, and Tartar's lips,
Finger of birth-strangled babe
Ditch-delivered by a drab,
Make the gruel thick and slab.

ALL: Double, double, toil and trouble;
Fire burn, and cauldron bubble.

SECOND WITCH: Cool it with a baboon's blood;
Then the charm is firm and good.

The three sisters perform charms and spells to conjure up evil spirits, which Macbeth then addresses. He begins to ask the apparitions questions, but he is silenced by the elder witch who tells him that he is here to listen, not to talk.

MACBETH: Tell me, thou unknown power -

FIRST WITCH: He knows thy thought.
Hear his speech but say nought.

The first apparition, an armored head, rises from the cauldron.

FIRST APPARITION: Macbeth, Macbeth, Macbeth, beware

Macduff!
Beware the Thane of Fife! Dismiss me. Enough.

The apparition vanishes and Macbeth thanks him, for the ghost has confirmed Macbeth's suspicions of Macduff, the Thane of Fife. Then the second spirit rises from the cauldron. It has the form of a bloody child.

SECOND APPARITION: Be bloody, bold and resolute. Laugh to scorn
The power of man, for none of woman born
Shall harm Macbeth.

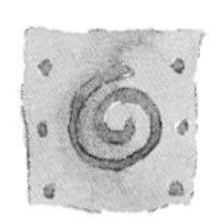

The second apparition vanishes too, leaving Macbeth to wonder why he need fear Macduff if, at the same time, no one of "woman born" will ever harm him. At this, the third spirit appears, this time in the form of a crowned child, holding a small tree. Macbeth wants to know if Banquo's heirs will become kings of Scotland.

THIRD APPARITION: Be lion-mettled, proud, and take no care
Who chafes, who frets, or where conspirers are:

Macbeth shall never vanquished be, until
Great Birnam wood to high Dunsinane Hill
Shall come against him.

MACBETH: That shall never be.
Who can impress the forest, bid the tree
Unfix his earth-bound root? Yet my heart
Throbs to know one thing. Tell me, if your art
Can tell so much, shall Banquo's issue ever
Reign in this kingdom?

ALL: Seek to know no more.

MACBETH: I will be satisfied! Deny me this
And an eternal curse fall on you. Let me know.

At this, strange music is heard and the cauldron slowly sinks into the earth.

ALL: Show his eyes and grieve his heart,
Come like shadows, so depart.

Now an entire procession of eight kings appears out of the air. The eighth resembles the murdered Banquo and carries a glass. He smiles at Macbeth as he passes and points to the glass. On it are depicted the images of future kings, the descendants of Banquo.

MACBETH: Now I see it is true

For the blood boltered Banquo smiles upon me
And points at them for his. What! Is this so?

FIRST WITCH: Ay, sir, all this is so.

The witches vanish and Lennox arrives to tell Macbeth that Macduff has fled to England. Enraged, Macbeth orders that Macduff's wife, children, and all those left behind in Macduff's castle, be slaughtered.

MACBETH: Seize upon Fife, give to the edge of the sword
His wife, his babes, and all unfortunate souls
That trace him in his line.

Meanwhile, Macduff has taken refuge in England and joined forces with Malcolm. Macduff laments Scotland's fate, unaware of his own personal loss.

MACDUFF: O Scotland, Scotland! O nation miserable,
With an untitled tyrant, bloody-sceptred,
When shalt thou see thy wholesome days again.

Macduff declares that Macbeth's tyranny cannot be allowed to continue, and Malcolm tells him that he has already raised an army of ten thousand soldiers. Just then Ross arrives with the news of the slaughter.

ROSS: Your castle is surprised, your wife and babes
Savagely slaughtered.

MALCOLM: Merciful heaven!
What, man! Ne'er pull your hat upon your brows,
Give sorrow words. The grief that does not speak
Whispers the o'erfraught heart and bids it break.

MACDUFF: My children too?

ROSS: Wife, children, servants, all
That could be found.

MACDUFF: My wife killed too?

ROSS: I have said.

MALCOLM: Be comforted.
Let's make us medicines of our great revenge
To cure this deadly grief.

MACDUFF: O I could play the woman with mine eyes
And braggart with my tongue But gentle heaven
Cut short all intermission. Front to front
Bring thou this fiend of Scotland and myself
Within my sword's length set him. If he escape
Heaven forgive him too.

MALCOLM: This tune goes manly.
Come, go we to the King. Our power is ready.
Our lack is nothing but our leave. Macbeth
is ripe for shaking, and the powers above
Put on their instruments.

Back in Scotland, Macbeth's increasingly barbaric behavior is taking its toll on Lady Macbeth. She has begun walking in her sleep and a doctor is called to observe her.

GENTLEWOMAN: Lo you, here she comes! This is her very guise, and upon my life, fast asleep.

DOCTOR: How came she by that light?

GENTLEWOMAN: Why, it stood by her. She has light by her continually, 'tis her command.

DOCTOR: You see her eyes are open.

GENTLEWOMAN: Ay, but their sense are shut.

DOCTOR: What is it she does now? Look how she rubs her hands.

GENTLEWOMAN: It is an accustomed action with her to seem thus washing her hands.
I have known her continue in this for a quarter of an hour.

LADY MACBETH: Look, here's a spot.

DOCTOR: Hark! She speaks.

LADY MACBETH: Out, damned spot! Out, I say! One, two: why then, 'tis time to do it. Hell is murky! Fie, my lord, fie! A soldier and afeard? What need we fear who knows it, when none can call our power to account? Yet who would have thought the old man to have had so much blood in him?

DOCTOR: Do you mark that?

LADY MACBETH: The Thane of Fife had a wife. Where is she now? What, will these hands never be clean?

Recognizing the sinister references, the doctor chides her attendant for hearing things that she should not.

DOCTOR: Go to, go to: you have known what you should not.

GENTLEWOMAN: She has spoke what she should not, I am sure of that. Heaven knows what she has known.

LADY MACBETH: Here's the smell of the blood still. All the perfumes of Arabia will not sweeten this little hand. Oh!

DOCTOR: What a sigh is there! This heart is sorely charged.

GENTLEWOMAN: I would not have such a heart in my bosom for the dignity of the whole body.

DOCTOR: This disorder is beyond my practice.

LADY MACBETH: Wash your hands, put on your night gown. Look not so pale. I tell you yet again, Banquo's buried: he cannot come out on's grave.

DOCTOR: Even so?

LADY MACBETH: To bed, to bed! There's knocking at the gate. Come, come, come, come, give me your hand. What's done cannot be undone. To bed, to bed, to bed.

DOCTOR: Foul whisperings are abroad, unnatural deeds
Do breed unnatural troubles. Infected minds
To their deaf pillows will discharge their secrets.
More needs she the divine than the physician.
God, God forgive us all!

The English army, with Malcolm and Macduff at its head, is now advancing on Dunsinane. Macbeth has for-

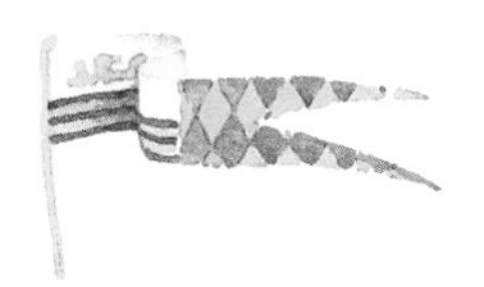

tified the castle, but has become increasingly desperate as reports indicate that support for him is dwindling fast. His behavior becomes increasingly irrational and unpredictable, and he falls back on the witches' prophecies to give him hope.

MACBETH: Till Birnam Wood remove to Dunsinane
I cannot taint with fear. What's the boy Malcolm?
Was he not born of woman? The spirits that know
All mortal consequences have pronounced me thus:
"Fear not, Macbeth. No man that's born of woman
Shall ere have power upon thee."

At this a forlorn servant enters.

SERVANT: Soldiers, sir. The English force, so please you.

MACBETH: Take thy face hence.

The servant flees.

MACBETH: I am sick at heart.
I have lived long enough. My way of life
Is fallen into the sere, the yellow leaf.
And that which should accompany old age,
As honour, love, obedience, troops of friends,
I must not look to have, but in their stead
Curses, not loud, but deep, mouth-honour, breath
Which the poor heart would fain deny and dare not.

The English army, advancing on Macbeth's stronghold, reaches Birnam Wood, mentioned in the witches' prophecy. Malcolm instructs each soldier to cut down a tree branch to use as camouflage. Macbeth, meanwhile, in a false bravado, continues to prepare Dunsinane Castle for the onslaught.

MACBETH: The cry is still, "They come." Our castle's strength
Will laugh a siege to scorn. Here let them lie
Till famine and the ague eat them up.

Suddenly a cry goes up inside the castle, and a servant

brings news to Macbeth that Lady Macbeth is dead. Macbeth sees the bleakness of his future.

SERVANT: The queen, my lord, is dead.

MACBETH: She should have died hereafter,
There would have been a time for such a word.
Tomorrow, and tomorrow, and tomorrow
Creeps in this petty pace from day to day,
To the last syllable of recorded time.
And all our yesterdays have lighted fools
The way to dusty death. Out, out, brief candle!
Life's but a walking shadow, a poor player
That struts and frets his hour upon the stage
And then is heard no more. It is a tale
Told by an idiot, full of sound and fury,
Signifying nothing.

Lady Macbeth's death seems to have dulled whatever appetite Macbeth may have had for the fight. A messenger arrives with more ominous news; the prophecy of Birnam Wood has been fulfilled.

MESSENGER: As I did stand my watch upon the hill,
I looked toward Birnam and anon methought
The wood began to move!

MACBETH: Liar and slave!

MESSENGER: Let me endure your wrath if it be not so.
Within this three mile may you see it coming.
I say, a moving grove!

MACBETH: If thou speak'st false,
Upon the next tree thou shall hang alive
Till famine cling thee...

In this resigned but warlike mood, Macbeth and his men sally forth from the castle and down the hillside toward the advancing army. The castle soon falls to the English force, while Macduff, desperate to avenge the murders of his wife and children, seeks out Macbeth.

MACDUFF: That way the noise is. Tyrant, show thy face.
If thou be'st slain, and with no stroke of mine,
My wife and children's ghosts will haunt me still.
I cannot strike at wretched Kerns, whose arms
Are hired to bear their staves. Either thou, Macbeth,
Or else my sword with an unbattered edge
I sheathe again undeeded. There thou shouldst be:
By this great clatter one of greatest note
Seems bruited. Let me find him, fortune!
And more I beg not.

At this moment he catches sight of Macbeth.

MACDUFF: Turn, hellhound, turn!

MACBETH: Of all men else I have avoided thee.
But get thee back; my soul is too much charged
With blood of thine already.

They begin to fight. Macbeth clings to his belief that he cannot be killed, not knowing that Macduff was not "of woman born".

MACBETH: Thou losest labour.
I bear a charmed life which must not yield
To one of woman born.

MACDUFF: Despair thy charm
And let the angel whom thou still hast served
Tell thee Macduff was from his mother's womb
Untimely ripped.

MACBETH: Accursed be that tongue that tells me so,
For it hath cowed my better part of man.
And be these juggling fiends no more believed
That palter with us in a double sense,
That keep the word of promise to our ear,
And break it to our hope.I'll not fight with thee.

MACDUFF: Then yield, thee coward,
And live to be the show and gaze o' the time.
We'll have thee, as our rarer monsters are,
Painted upon a pole, and underwrit,

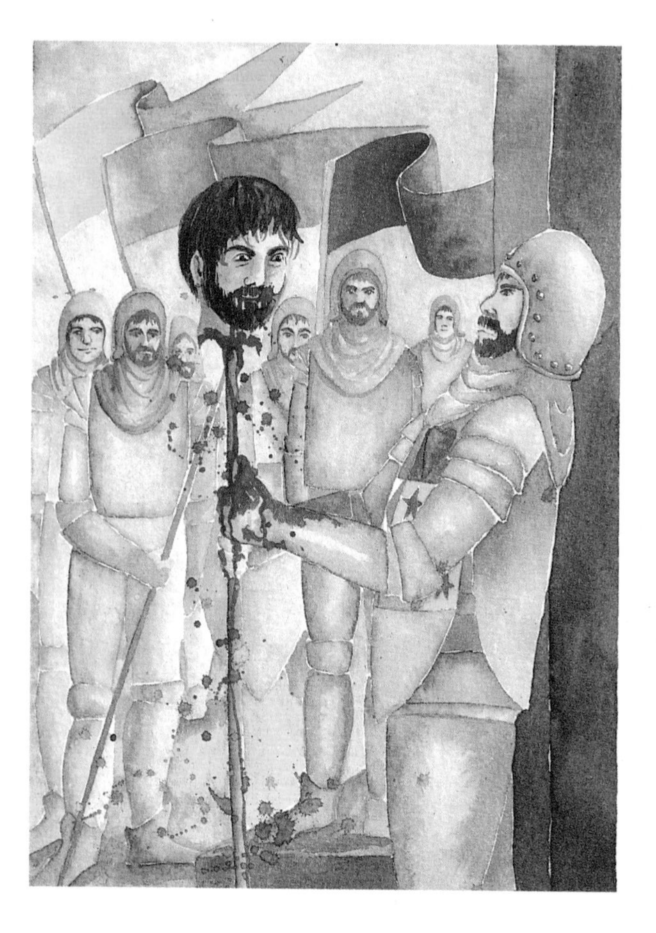

"Here may you see the tyrant."

MACBETH: I will not yield
To kiss the ground before young Malcolm's feet
And to be baited with the rabble's curse.
And thou opposed, being of no woman born,
Yet I will try the last. Before my body
I throw my warlike shield. Lay on Macduff,
And damned him that first cries, "Hold, enough!"

In the struggle, Macbeth is slain. Macduff parades Macbeth's severed head, fixed upon his own sword, for all to see, and hails Malcolm as the new king. Malcolm in his turn, vows to restore peace and order to Scotland, and looks forward to happier times for his new subjects.

MALCOLM: My thanes and kinsmen,
Henceforth be earls, the first that ever Scotland
In such an honour named. What's more to do,
Which would be planted newly with the time,
As calling home our exiled friends abroad
That fled the snares of watchful tyranny,
Producing forth the cruel ministers
Of this dead butcher and his fiend-like queen -
Who, as 'tis thought, by self and violent hands
Took off her life - this, and what needful else
That calls upon us, by the grace of Grace
We will perform in measure, time, and place.

So thanks to all at once, and to each one,
Whom we invite to see us crowned at Scone.

Glossary

ague: fever

avaunt: be off, leave

badged: marked

bruited: reported

casing: enclosing

choppy: rough

chough: jackdaw (a bird)

chuck: hen (term of endearment)

compunctious: remorseful

dam: mother

drab: whore

earnest: pledge

ere: before

fenny: of the fen (marsh land)

fit: sudden attack of illness

gild: coat

howlet: young owl

hurly-burly: chaotic activity

incarnadine: to dye or stain with a red color

Kerns: Irish mercenaries

prithee: pray you, please

sere: withered

sleek: smooth

surcease: cessation